THIS YEARBOOK
BELONGS TO

THE YEARBOOK FOR GIRLS

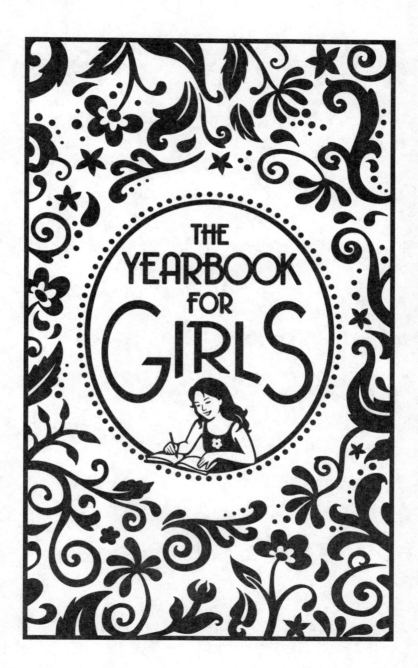

Written by Ellen Bailey
Illustrated by Nellie Ryan

Edited by Liz Scoggins
Designed by Angie Allison

THE YEARBOOK FOR GIRLS

Buster Books

NOTE TO READERS

The publisher and author disclaim all liability, as far as is legally permitted, for any accidents or injuries or loss that may occur as a result of the use or misuse of the information and guidance given in this book.

We urge you, at all times, to make yourself aware of, and obey, all laws, regulations and local by-laws, and respect all rights, including the rights of property owners. Always respect other people's privacy and remember to ask a responsible adult for assistance and take their advice whenever necessary. Above all, remember to exercise good common sense and take all necessary safety precautions when preparing to attempt an activity, particularly when using scissors and glue.

First published in Great Britain in 2010 by Buster Books,
an imprint of Michael O'Mara Books Limited,
9 Lion Yard, Tremadoc Road, London SW4 7NQ

www.mombooks.com/busterbooks

Cover design by Angie Allison
Cover illustration by Nellie Ryan

A CIP catalogue record for this book is available from the British Library.

ISBN: 978-1-906082-82-6

2 4 6 8 10 9 7 5 3 1

Printed and bound in England by Clays Ltd, St Ives plc

Papers used by Buster Books are natural, recyclable products made from wood grown in sustainable forests. The manufacturing processes conform to the environmental regulations of the country of origin.

CONTENTS

Getting started 7

This book is all about me 8

Making your memory box 10

Right here, right now 13

Taking the measure 14

Look to the future 17

What will be, will be 18

Your Egyptian horoscope 19

Ten things to achieve this year 23

Mood calculator 24

Mirror, mirror 25

Ten things to stop worrying about this year 26

That's so annoying! 27

Top ten things I like about me 28

Superfan or superstar? 29

All in a night's sleep 30

Sweet dreams 32

Funniest things of all time 33

Fashion favourites 34

What's your style? 36

Your style answers 38

Prince Charming 39

Which boy is for me? 40

Boys – friends or foes? 42

Love it, hate it 43

Best names ever 45

Scholastic fantastic 46

Career day 47

Career-day answers 49

Most likely to ... 50

Under pressure 54

Under-pressure answers 57

Free-time favourites 58

TV addict 59

Best books of all time 60

What do your doodles do? 61

Your doodle answers 64

Scariest things of all time 67

Fight the fear 68
Are you a money master? 69
Money-master answers 71
Music mixes 72
Fantasy band on tour 74
Travel tales 76
Ultimate destination 77
Miss this 78
Don't miss that 79
Forever foods 80
Are you a daredevil? 81
Daring answers 82
Top ten people you admire 83
Your 'influences' clock 85
Family fortunes 86
In-depth interview 88
Party planner 92
Personal profiler 94
Your personal profile answers 96
Best games of all time 97
Four seasons in one page 98
If I were ... 99
Superpower showdown 100
Your superhero costume 101
Guilty pleasures 102
Body tricks 103
Fingerprint fun 104
How's your 'holistic' health? 106
Ultimate confessions 108
Best friends forever? 109
Agony-aunt challenge 111
Pet profile 113
A few of my favourite things 114
Survival skills 115
Survival answers 116
Would you rather? 117
Best moments of all time 119
Headline news 120
Headline-maker 121
Sign of the times 122
Social butterfly or butterflies in your tummy? 123
Friendship gallery 124
The film of your life ... 126
Best films of all time 127

GETTING STARTED

This book is about to change your life. Inside, you will find tons of quizzes and questions that will make you think and make you laugh. As you fill in the blank spaces, you'll be making a record of exactly who you are this year. Treasure it forever.

You don't have to read this book in any particular order, as each section you fill in has a space to make a note of the date, time and place, like this:

Date .... Time .... Place ....

Each time there's a quiz or questionnaire, you'll need to fill out your opinion along the dotted line:

like this
....

or tick the box next to the answer you most agree with, like this:

Yes ✓ No ◯

MEMORY BOX MEMENTOS

Follow the instructions on pages 10–12 to make a Memory Box. Use it to store all sorts of things, from '**Memory Box Memento**' suggestions throughout this book, to ideas of your own. When this book is complete, store it in the Memory Box, too, so you'll know just where to look to remember this incredible year.

THIS BOOK IS ALL ABOUT ME

My name is ....

My nickname is ....

My birthday is on ....

I was born in the year ....

The place I was born is called ....

My star sign is ....

Right now I'm .... years old

I got this book on ....

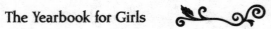

My mum's name is ....

My dad's name is ....

I have .... brothers and .... sisters

Their names are ....

....

My school is called ....

My best friend is ....

I have .... pets

Signed ....

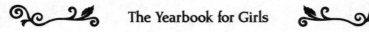

MAKING YOUR MEMORY BOX

Your Memory Box will be the perfect place to keep all sorts of treasured mementos that you can look back at in the future. It's simple to make, just follow the instructions below. First, think about the kind of style you want to create when decorating your Memory Box. Choose giftwrap with a vintage pattern, such as Victorian flowers for a classic feel, shiny metallics to create a futuristic style, or an up-to-date pattern to reflect the current year.

You will need:

• a cardboard box with a lid (a shoebox is perfect) • patterned giftwrap • plain giftwrap • a ruler • a pencil • scissors • a glue stick • PVA glue • ribbon • a selection of sequins and buttons

1. On the back of the plain giftwrap, draw a rectangle that measures the same as the width and height of your box. Add 2 cm extra along the top and bottom, to fold around the top edge and on to the base of the box.

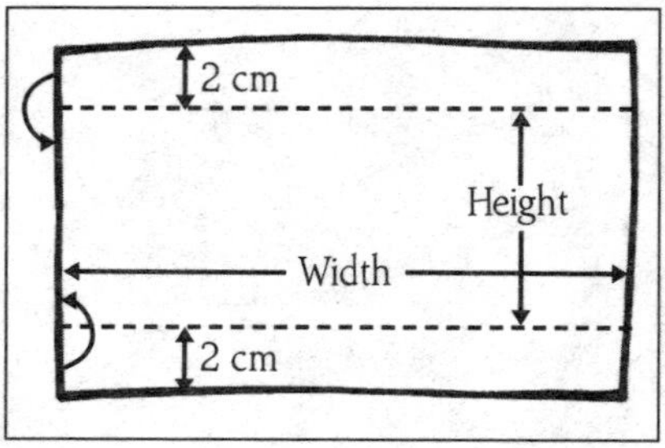

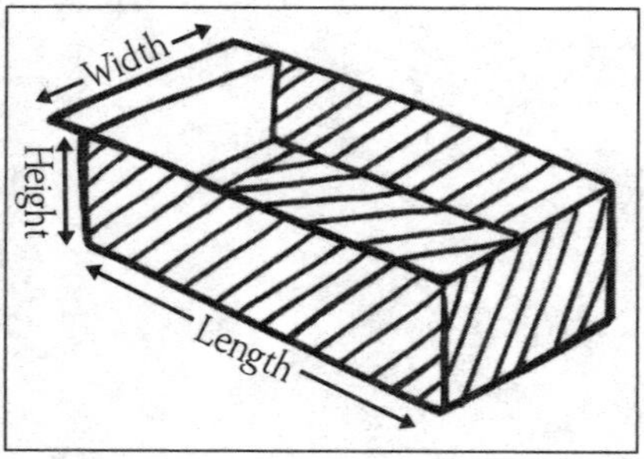

2. Draw another rectangle, exactly the same as the first, and cut them both out. Use your glue stick to glue one to the inside of each end of the box, as shown here.

3. Now draw another rectangle to line the base and the two long sides of the box. It should measure the same as the length of the box by the width and two times the height. Remember to add 2 cm extra at each end to overlap the edges.

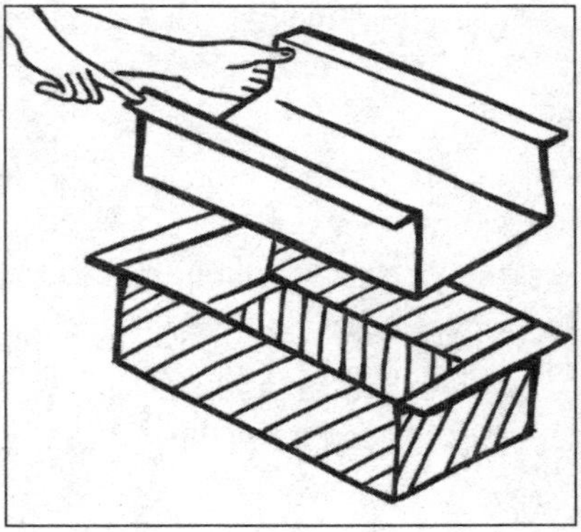

4. Add a layer of glue all over the base and the two long sides, then stick this strip in place.

5. Next, lay your patterned giftwrap, right-side down, on a flat surface. Place the box on top and draw around the base. Add 2 cm extra on each side to fold around the sides of the box.

6. Glue this rectangle to the bottom of the box and stick the edges on to the sides.

7. Now measure a strip of the patterned giftwrap to cover all four sides. You may need to do this in two pieces if your paper is not long enough. Neatly glue the strip to the sides of the box.

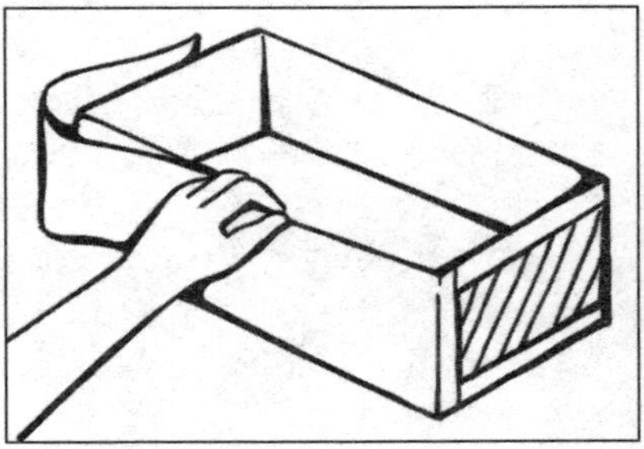

8. Cover the lid in the same way.

9. Take another piece of plain giftwrap. On the back, write the words 'Memory Box' backwards in large bubble letters, like this:

10. Carefully cut out the letters and glue them onto the lid of the box. Get an adult to help you cut out the centres of the letters if you need to, as this bit can be quite tricky.

11. Last of all, decorate the lid and the sides of the box with your selection of sequins, buttons and glitter. Arrange them in a pattern you like, then use a dab of PVA glue to secure each one.

12. Once the glue has dried thoroughly, tie your length of ribbon around the box in a bow to keep the lid secure.

Put your Memory Box in a safe place, such as the bottom of your wardrobe. Pop any items that you'd like to keep in it, as well as any ideas you like from the **Memory Box Memento** suggestions.

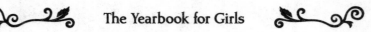

RIGHT HERE, RIGHT NOW

Date ....

Time ....

Place ....

Use this page to make a record of what you are doing at this exact moment in time.

What sounds can you hear right now?

....

What are you wearing? ....

....

How have you done your hair? ....

....

Who are you with? ....

What is the weather like? ....

....

What can you see right now? ....

....

What's in your pocket? ....

TAKING THE MEASURE

Date .... Time .... Place ....

Fill in your answers below, using whichever units of measurement you prefer – for instance, you can measure your height in feet and inches or in metres and centimetres.

Height. How tall are you? ....

How tall would you like to be? ....

Eyes. Most people say their eyes are blue, brown, green or hazel. However, if you take a close look in the mirror you'll see flecks of all sorts of other colours in your irises – the coloured part of your eye. Use a set of coloured pencils in the picture below to show how many colours you can really see.

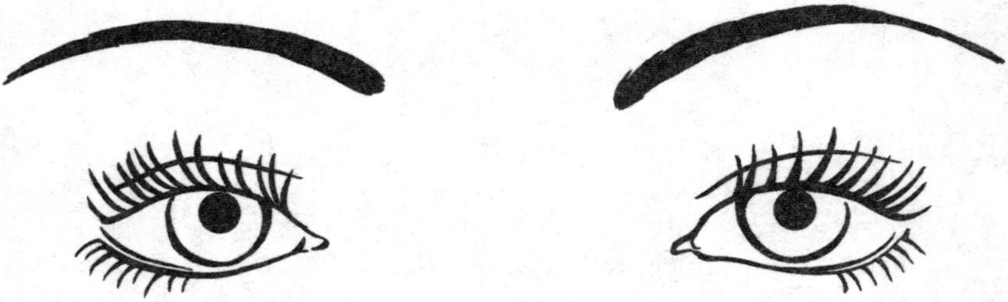

Hands. Spread your fingers out as wide as they can go. What is the distance from the tip of your thumb to the tip of your little finger?

....

How long is your hand from the tip of your middle finger to the bottom of your palm?

What is the length of your little finger?

Feet. Did you know that the distance from your heel to the tip of your big toe is usually the same as the distance from your wrist to your elbow? Try it to see.

What is the distance from your heel to the tip of your big toe?

What is the distance from your wrist to your elbow?

Are both your feet exactly the same length? Yes ◌ No ◌

What colour would you most like to paint your toes? Use coloured pencils to decorate this set of nails.

Ears. How long are your ears? ....

Is one higher than the other? Yes ◯ No ◯

Nose. What is the distance from between your eyes to the tip of your nose?

....

Do you think your nose is:

Too big ◯ Too small ◯ Just right ◯ ?

Hair. How long is a strand of your hair?

....

How long would you like it to be? ....

In years to come, you can take the same measurements again to see how much you have changed.

Memory Box Memento. Next time you visit the hairdressers, keep a lock of your hair. Tie a length of thread around it to keep it together, then find a small box or envelope to put it in, and pop it in your Memory Box.

LOOK TO THE FUTURE

Date .... Time .... Place ....

In ten years' time I want to

live in .... with

.... My pet will be a

.... called .... I want to be able to

.... My greatest achievement will

be ....

I will have met .... in real life.

My most treasured possession will be my

....

WHAT WILL BE, WILL BE

Date .... Time .... Place ....

What do you think the future will be like? What things do you think will be more popular, and what do you think will be less popular? Perhaps you think that recycling will be going up, and cars will be going down. Or maybe dogs will be going up, and cats will be going down? Fill the arrows below with your predictions.

Going Up

....

....

....

....

....

Going Down

....

....

....

....

Memory Box Memento. Cut pictures out of magazines of things that you want to have in the future, such as a cool car or exotic holidays. Stick them on a piece of paper to make a collage. Add decorations and words from the magazines, too.

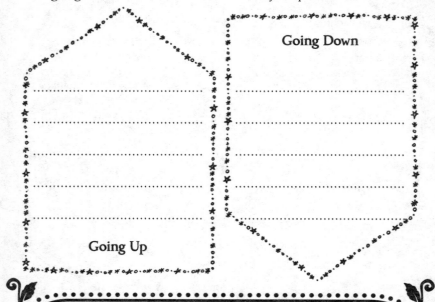

YOUR EGYPTIAN HOROSCOPE

Date .... Time .... Place ....

You're probably familiar with the kind of horoscopes that appear every day in newspapers. You might even know your Chinese horoscope, based on the year of your birth, but you may not have come across many Egyptian horoscopes before.

The ancient Egyptians believed that the exact position of the stars on the day you were born would affect your destiny and give you characteristics of the god whose sign you were born under. Here's what a horoscope might have been like at the time of the pharaohs – what does your Egyptian horoscope say about you?

Thoth – god of learning
29th August – 27th September

People born under Thoth are usually clever and good at solving problems. You love organizing fun activities for your friends and you're spontaneous and full of original ideas.

Horus – god of the sky
28th September – 27th October

If you were born under Horus, you are likely to have great ambitions that you'll need to work hard to achieve. You are also brave, sociable, motivated and outgoing.

Wadjet – protector goddess
28th October – 26th November

You are loyal and unselfish, and always stand up for your friends. You tend to approach new things with caution and think them through clearly first.

Sekhmet – goddess of war
27th November – 26th December

You are likely to be fiercely intelligent. Your friends love your brilliant sense of humour and that you can remain optimistic through tough times. You are imaginative and energetic.

Sphinx – goddess of treasure
27th December – 25th January

Those born under this sign can often adapt to any situation. You're good at keeping secrets and your friends aren't afraid to share their problems with you. You are also tidy, organized and intelligent.

Shu – god of air
26th January – 24th February

People born under Shu are often very creative. You are good at sorting out problems between your friends and hate seeing people upset. You are fair, kind and have a good sense of humour.

Isis – goddess of mothers
25th February – 26th March

People born under Isis are usually excellent listeners. You make friends easily and don't judge people. You are trustworthy, straightforward and reliable.

Osiris – god of the afterlife
27th March – 25th April

You are brilliant at coming up with new and exciting ideas. Your friends love your sense of adventure. You are intelligent and lively, so nothing is ever dull when you're around.

Amun – god of creation
26th April – 25th May

If you were born under this sign, you are likely to be strong and brave. Your confidence makes you a born leader and your friends often come to you for advice.

Hathor – goddess of music, dance and joy
26th May – 24th June

People born under the sign of Hathor have a serious romantic streak. As well as being emotional and passionate, you are likely to be popular and have lots of close friends.

Phoenix – bird-god of new life
25th June – 24th July

If you were born under this sign, you are especially good at turning difficult situations into wonderful new beginnings. Your friends love your sunny personality and upbeat, optimistic nature.

Anubis – guardian-god of the dead
25th July – 28th August

People born under Anubis are likely to be protectors who look after people. Your friends admire your confidence and determination. You are generous and kind, and never give up.

Memory Box Memento. First, read what your Egyptian horoscope says about you. Then take a piece of paper and write your own predictions for what might happen to you in the future. Imagine what subjects you might choose to study, who you will go out with when you're older, where you might live and so on. Seal your predictions inside an envelope and write on the date you are allowed to open it in the future. Tuck it away at the bottom of your Memory Box, but don't forget to check if your predicitons came true.

TEN THINGS TO ACHIEVE THIS YEAR

Date .... Time .... Place ....

Try to achieve each of these ideas within the year and tick each one off as soon as you manage it. If there is something you particularly want to try that isn't on the list, make a note of it at the bottom of the page and tick it off once you have succeeded, too.

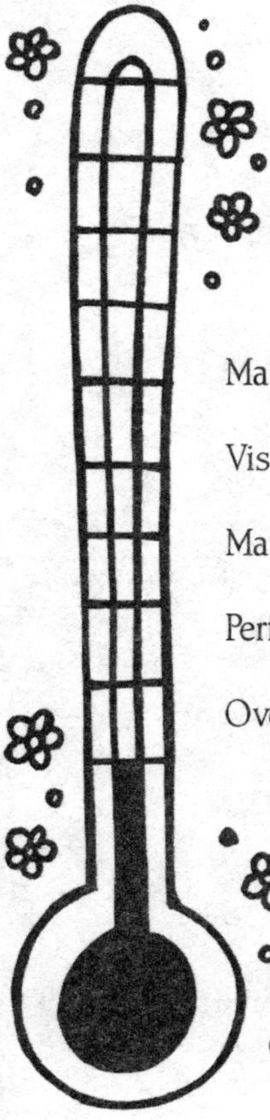

- Raise some money for charity ◯
- Laugh so hard my sides hurt ◯
- Grow a plant from seed ◯
- Master a recipe ◯
- Make at least one completely new friend ◯
- Visit a place I've never been to before ◯
- Make someone a birthday present from scratch ◯
- Perform something in public ◯
- Overcome one of my fears ◯
- Start keeping a journal ◯

....

.... ◯

MOOD CALCULATOR

Date .... Time .... Place ....

Use this section to unload anything you like.

Is anything annoying you right now? Yes ◯ No ◯

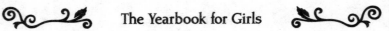

If 'Yes', what is it? ....

....

....

What are you happiest about right now?

....

....

Are you worried about anything? Yes ◯ No ◯

If 'Yes', what is it? ....

....

Who did you last argue with?

....

What about? ....

Have you made up yet? Yes ◯ No ◯

MIRROR, MIRROR

Date .... Time .... Place ....

Draw a picture of yourself in the mirror below, then write four words that describe how you're feeling today around the outside.

....

....

TEN THINGS TO STOP WORRYING ABOUT THIS YEAR

Date .... Time .... Place ....

This year, why not make a resolution (a promise to yourself) to worry less? Think of all the things that are most likely to make you bite your nails or chew your lip. List them in order, so that the most worrying thing is at number one. Once you've written things down, they'll probably seem less worrying already ...

1. ....

2. ....

3. ....

4. ....

5. ....

6. ....

7. ....

8. ....

9. ....

10. ....

THAT'S SO ANNOYING!

Date .... Time .... Place ....

Write down four things that really annoy you in the first row, such as wasps or people kicking the back of your chair. Choose which thing from each pair is the most annoying, then decide which of the final two is the thing that annoys you most of all in the world.

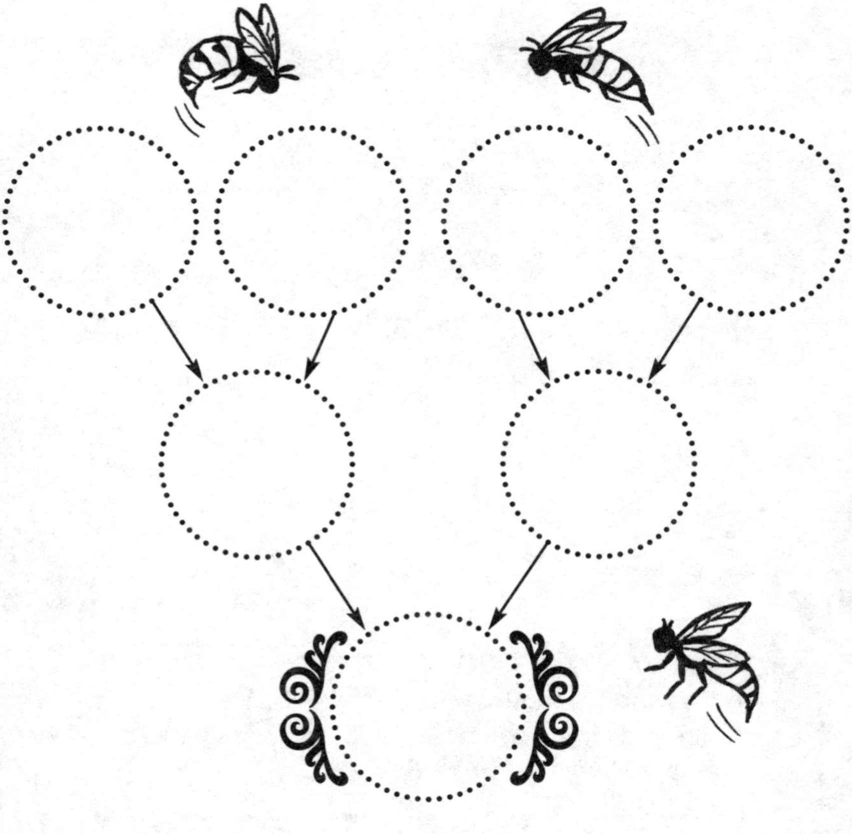

TOP TEN THINGS I LIKE ABOUT ME

Date .... Time .... Place ....

Organize the ten things you like most about yourself into a top ten, according to how you rate each point, with the best at number one.

1. ....
2. ....
3. ....
4. ....
5. ....
6. ....
7. ....
8. ....
9. ....
10. ....

Memory Box Memento. With a friend, write a list of the top ten things you like about each other. Swap lists and keep her list about you in your Memory Box.

SUPERFAN OR SUPERSTAR?

Date .... Time .... Place ....

Do you think you're more likely to become a superstar or a superfan? It's time to make up your mind – study each option and tick your preference.

Shop online ◯	Personal shopper ◯
Fish fingers ◯	Oysters ◯
Photographer ◯	Model ◯
Takeaway ◯	Restaurant ◯
Milk chocolate ◯	Dark chocolate ◯
Roadie ◯	Lead singer ◯
Shower ◯	Bubblebath ◯
Trainers ◯	High-heels ◯
Autograph hunter ◯	Autograph signer ◯
Good friends ◯	Entourage ◯
Kitten ◯	Lapdog ◯
Minibus ◯	Tour bus ◯

ALL IN A NIGHT'S SLEEP

Date .... Time .... Place ....

Complete this questionnaire to record your sleeping habits.

- Do you share your bedroom? Yes ◯ No ◯
- If 'yes', who with? ....
- Blankets ◯ Duvet ◯ ?
- What colour? ....
- What time do you normally go to bed? ....
- How many hours sleep do you normally get each night?

  .... hours.
- How long do you brush your teeth for?

  .... minutes .... seconds
- Floss ◯ Mouthwash ◯ ?
- What do you wear to bed? ....

  ....
- Do you read for a while ◯ Watch TV for a while ◯ ?
- Do you leave the door open ◯ Leave the window open ◯ ?

Do you sleep:

On your side ◌ On your back ◌ On your front ◌ ?

When you wake up in the morning does your bedding look like:

You've fought a monster ◌ ?

You've slept perfectly still, like Sleeping Beauty ◌ ?

Somewhere in between these two things ◌ ?

Have you ever:

Fallen out of bed ◌ ?

Woken up with your feet at the pillow end ◌ ?

Wriggled so much that your sheets came off in the night ◌ ?

SWEET DREAMS

Date .... Time .... Place ....

Anything is possible in dreams. Think of your five favourites and write them out in order, so that the best dream is at number one.

1. ....

....

2. ....

....

3. ....

....

4. ....

....

5. ....

....

Memory Box Memento. Make a record of a week in your dreams. Cut two sheets of A4 card into quarters. Write the date and describe each night's dream on each card. Draw a picture of the dream on the back then punch a hole in the top left-hand corner. Tie them together with a length of pretty ribbon.

FUNNIEST THINGS OF ALL TIME

Date .... Time .... Place ....

Think of the ten funniest things that have ever happened to you, that you've seen in a film or on TV, or your favourite jokes. Organize them into a top ten, with your favourite at number one.

1. ....

2. ....

3. ....

4. ....

5. ....

6. ....

7. ....

8. ....

9. ....

....

10. ....

....

....

FASHION FAVOURITES

Date .... Time .... Place ....

Tick your favourite item from each category below, then draw your favourite outfit on the mannequin opposite.

Necklines. Halter ◯ V-neck ◯ Square ◯ Round ◯

Hats. Beret ◯ Baseball cap ◯ Straw hat ◯ Bobble hat ◯

Fabrics. Silk ◯ Cotton ◯ Denim ◯ Wool ◯

Jewellery. Sparkly ◯ Wooden ◯ Gold ◯ Silver ◯

Shopping. Internet ◯ High street ◯ Market ◯ Boutique ◯

Shoes. Flip-flops ◯ Trainers ◯ High-heels ◯ Pumps ◯

Bags. Beach ◯ Clutch ◯ Backpack ◯ Basket ◯

Coats. Duffle ◯ Denim ◯ Waterproof ◯ Leather ◯

Clothing. High street ◯ Designer ◯ Vintage ◯ Home-made ◯

Style. Urban ◯ Sporty ◯ Romantic ◯ Preppy ◯

Prints. Bright ◯ Flowery ◯ Animal ◯ Geometric ◯

Jeans. Skinny ◯ Flared ◯ Baggy ◯ Boot-cut ◯

Warmth. Cardigan ◯ Shawl ◯ Body warmer ◯ Scarf ◯

In bed. Pyjamas ◯ T-shirt ◯ Nightie ◯ Vest and shorts ◯

Inspiration. Friends ◯ Celebs ◯ Adverts ◯ Music ◯

MY FAVOURITE OUTFIT

Choose items of clothing you already own, or pieces that you'd just love to have to complete your perfect outfit.

Use the space around the mannequin to describe the fabrics and what the outfit is for, or even to draw patterns or describe textures in more detail.

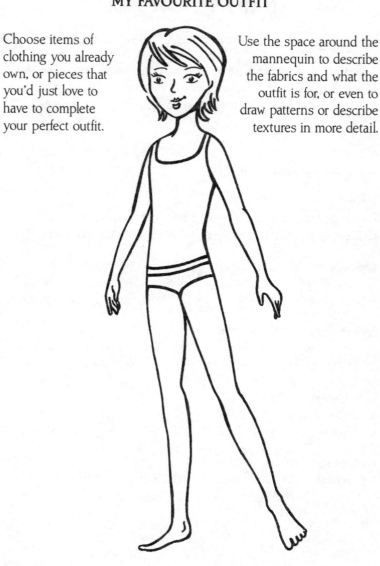

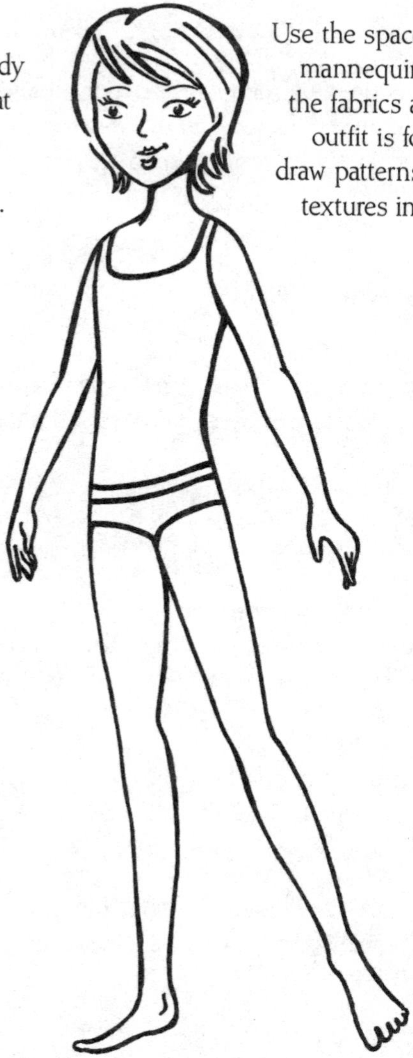

WHAT'S YOUR STYLE?

Date .... Time .... Place ....

Take this quiz to find out more about yourself and your style. Make a note of the number of **a**s, **b**s, **c**s and **d**s you get as you go along and check out what your results mean on page 38. Here goes ...

Hair. Would you rather ...
a. ... it gets you noticed?
b. ... keep it out of the way?
c. ... keep it long and shiny?
d. ... not worry about it at all?

Lifestyle. Would you rather ...
a. ... spend a day as a film star?
b. ... spend a day as an athlete?
c. ... spend a day as a designer?
d. ... spend a day as a professor?

Clothes. Would you rather ...
a. ... stand out in bright colours?
b. ... have trainers at the ready?
c. ... be pretty in pink?
d. ... blend into the background?

Going out. Would you rather ...
a. ... sing lots of karaoke solos?
b. ... whizz around in a go-kart?
c. ... head for the shops?
d. ... explore a museum?

Homework. Would you rather ...
a. ... make it look really good?
b. ... do it as quickly as you can?
c. ... paint your toenails first?
d. ... take time to do it well?

Lunchtime. Would you rather ...
a. ... rehearse the school play?
b. ... join a game of football?
c. ... sit and people-watch?
d. ... head for the library?

Evenings. Would you rather ...
a. ... plan tomorrow's outfit? **b.** ... go to a sports club?
c. ... try out a new hairstyle? **d.** ... watch a documentary?

Friends. Would you rather be ...
a. ... leader of the pack? **b.** ... mates with the whole team?
c. ... one of the girls? **d.** ... best friends forever?

Superstar. Would you rather ...
a. ... have star quality? **b.** ... be faster than anyone else?
c. ... be completely glamorous? **d.** ... be a total genius?

The future. Would you rather ...
a. ... become a popstar? **b.** ... make the Olympic team?
c. ... become super-rich? **d.** ... win a Nobel Prize?

Away from home. Would you rather ...
a. ... go to drama camp? **b.** ... go on an adventure holiday?
c. ... lie in the sun? **d.** ... take in the city sights?

If you were a boy! Would you rather ...
a. ... be lead singer in a band? **b.** ... join the rugby team?
c. ... style your hair all day? **d.** ... spend the day studying?

YOUR STYLE ANSWERS

(Mostly **as.**) **Fun and flamboyant.** You have plenty of confidence, and don't mind standing out from the crowd. You might surprise a lot of people with your softer side, so don't forget to let it show sometimes.

(Mostly **bs.**) **Sporty miss.** You have bags of energy and can't help but be outgoing. You love to try new things, and make friends easily. Don't forget to take a break every now and then, to give yourself the chance to relax.

(Mostly **cs.**) **Party princess.** You love to spend time on your appearance, and enjoy being pampered. That doesn't mean you don't have a serious side, and you'll often surprise your friends and family with your clever and witty observations.

(Mostly **ds.**) **Ahead of the game.** You're very organized and usually like to make sure you're on top of things. Your parents and teachers probably appreciate how hard you study. Although you like to look before you leap, remember to save time to have fun with friends.

PRINCE CHARMING

Date .... Time .... Place ....

Ever wondered how you'll recognize your Prince Charming when he comes along? Rank the personality qualities below from 1–5, so you know exactly what you're looking for in the perfect partner.

Not Important ←1 2 3 4 5→ Really important

	1	2	3	4	5
Funny	○	○	○	○	○
Confident	○	○	○	○	○
Intelligent	○	○	○	○	○
Mature	○	○	○	○	○
Practical	○	○	○	○	○
Cool	○	○	○	○	○
Ambitious	○	○	○	○	○
Enthusiastic	○	○	○	○	○
Modest	○	○	○	○	○
Sensitive	○	○	○	○	○
Easy-going	○	○	○	○	○
Independent	○	○	○	○	○

WHICH BOY IS FOR ME?

Date .... Time .... Place ....

Have you ever wondered which boy you might be destined to go out with in the future? Work it out using the steps below.

1. First, write different boys' names in each of the flower petals on the opposite page.

2. Count the number of letters in your first name, and add it to the number of letters in your surname.

3. Divide this number by two. If you end up with a half number round it up. (For example, if you get 5.5, round it up to 6).

4. Starting at the top petal, count round the flower petals until you reach your number, then colour in that petal.

5. Continue counting on the following uncoloured petals, skipping any that are already coloured in. Every time you reach your number, colour in that petal.

6. When there is only one petal left uncoloured, that's your boy – well, maybe!

Memory Box Memento. If you have one, pop a photo of your favourite boy into your Memory Box. To remind yourself what you like about him, describe his best qualities on the back and any favourite moments you have shared. If you haven't met him yet, write where you would go on an ideal first date.

BOYS – FRIENDS OR FOES?

Date .... Time .... Place ....

Ask your friends to suggest ten famous boys for you. Write each name in one of the spaces below. Think about each boy and decide whether you would be friends, foes or love him forever. 'Undecided' is not an option.

	Friend	**Foe**	**Forever**
....	○	○	○
....	○	○	○
....	○	○	○
....	○	○	○
....	○	○	○
....	○	○	○
....	○	○	○
....	○	○	○
....	○	○	○
....	○	○	○

LOVE IT, HATE IT

Date .... Time .... Place ....

Colour in the hearts below. Use pink if you love what's written inside the heart, blue if you hate it, and yellow if you don't feel strongly either way.

Films at the cinema

Boys

Shopping

Being neat and tidy

Karaoke

Spicy food

Horoscopes

Camping

Chatting with friends

Fairground rides

BEST NAMES EVER

Date .... Time .... Place ....

List your ten favourite girls' names and your ten favourite boys' names. Organize each list into a top ten, according to how much you love them, so that your favourites are at number one.

Girls' Names	**Boys' Names**
1.	**1.** ....
2.	**2.** ....
3.	**3.** ....
4.	**4.** ....
5.	**5.** ....
6.	**6.** ....
7.	**7.** ....
8.	**8.** ....
9.	**9.** ....
10.	**10.** ....

Is your own name on the list? Yes ◯ No ◯

Would you change it to 'name **1.**' if you could? Yes ◯ No ◯

SCHOLASTIC FANTASTIC

Date .... Time .... Place ....

People often say that school days are the best days of your life, but what really goes on at your school?

- I love it at school when ....
- I hate it at school when ....
- My school uniform is okay ◯ awful ◯ I don't have one ◯
- The best school trip I've ever been on was to ....

  ....
- My favourite subject is ....
- The funniest person in my class is ....
- My favourite teacher is ....
- I last got in trouble because I ....

  ....
- My best excuse for being late is ....

  ....
- I eat my lunch with ....
- At break time, I like to ....

CAREER DAY

Date .... Time .... Place ....

Answer these questions to discover your career destiny. As you go along, make a note of each time you answer **a**, **b**, **c** or **d**. Then turn to page 49 for your results.

From the following subjects, which is your favourite?

a. Art.
b. P.E.
c. Drama.
d. Science.

Which of these holidays would you prefer?

a. Relaxing in a beautiful country cottage.
b. Camping somewhere with stunning scenery.
c. Staying at a hotel in a stylish, fast-paced city.
d. Visiting amazing ancient buildings in distant locations.

What are you most likely to be in charge of in a group project?

a. Drawing illustrations and creating charts.
b. Presenting the project to the class at the end.
c. Taking the lead and managing the project.
d. Researching the project and providing the key facts.

❁ How would you help your best friend celebrate her birthday?

a. Invite a few of her very best friends round for a sleepover.
b. Arrange a big picnic in the park.
c. Invite everyone she knows to the party of the year.
d. Take her to a show she's been talking about for ages.

❁ If you were an animal, which would you be?

a. A chimpanzee.
b. A horse.
c. A kitten.
d. A lion.

❁ Which of the following would you most like to win?

a. The Nobel Peace Prize.
b. A gold medal at the Olympics.
c. Personality of the Year.
d. The 'Women in Science' award.

❁ Which of these desserts would you most like to eat?

a. A big chocolate brownie.
b. An ice lolly.
c. A banana split.
d. A strawberry tart.

❁ Which of the following gifts would you most like to receive?

a. A playlist put together by your best friend.
b. A trip to a theme park.
c. A new mobile phone.
d. A computer game.

CAREER-DAY ANSWERS

(Mostly **as**.) **People person.** Thoughtful and creative – you'd make a brilliant interior designer, illustrator or novelist. Any career working with people would be ideal, too – perhaps as a teacher, a therapist or a carer.

(Mostly **bs**.) **Outdoor girl.** You love rolling up your sleeves to get stuck in. A job as a nature conservationist would be perfect, but you could also consider becoming a landscape gardener, a set designer or a journalist.

(Mostly **cs**.) **'Celeb'-in-waiting.** Of all the personality types, you're the most likely to become famous. You love to plan outings, so you'd be brilliant at public relations (organizing events such as book launches, restaurant openings, or press conferences). You could even work as a TV presenter or host your own radio show.

(Mostly **ds**.) **High-flyer.** You know your own mind and aren't afraid to study hard to make your dreams come true. You're destined for a career that makes lots of money and will earn you respect. A career as a doctor, architect, lawyer or banker would be perfect for you.

MOST LIKELY TO ...

Date .... Time .... Place ....

It's time to nominate your favourite people for a set of very special prizes. Do you have a friend who's always one step ahead of the latest trend and is bound to become a fashion icon? Or perhaps you have a relative who loves to be the centre of attention and is sure to end up on television?

In each of these frames, draw a picture or glue a photo of the person you think should receive each of the awards listed below. Don't forget to write the name underneath each portrait.

Who is most likely to ...

... win a Nobel Prize?

... appear on TV?

....

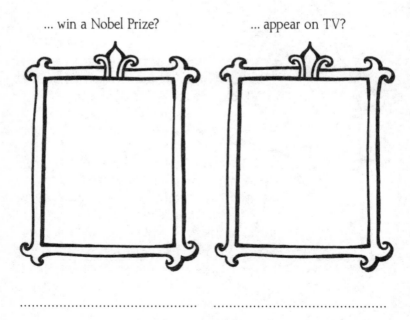

... get detention?

... become a millionaire?

... run a marathon?

... write a novel?

... break a bone?

....

... publish their memoirs?

....

... work with animals?

....

... become a fashion icon?

....

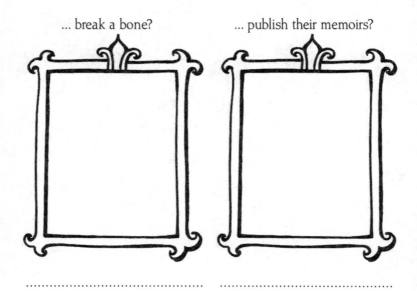

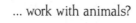

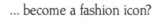

... trip on the red carpet?

....

... raise their hand in class?

....

UNDER PRESSURE

Date ....

Time .... Place ....

In a difficult situation, are you as cool as a cucumber or as wobbly as jelly? Answer these questions, and make a note of the number of **a**s, **b**s, **c**s and **d**s you get. Then turn the page to find out your results.

- On a Friday afternoon, your teacher announces that everyone must present a project to the class on Monday. How does this make you feel?

  a. Your heart starts pounding and your hands feel sweaty – you'll have to pretend to be ill.
  b. Eek! That sounds scary, but you know that if you work hard on it all weekend it'll be okay.
  c. No problem – you've got a great idea for the project and know you'll get a good mark.
  d. You certainly won't spend any time worrying about it – you'll just tell a few jokes and hope for the best.

- Your dad is driving you to meet your friends at the cinema when the car breaks down. How do you react?

  a. Moan at him for making you miss out and sulk all evening.
  b. Ask him to take you on the bus instead.

c. Text your friends to ask them to wait until the next showing.
d. Go for a burger with your dad instead.

✿ On a bowling trip with your family, your parents say they'll give a pocket-money bonus to the winner. How do you perform?

a. You try hard, but don't enjoy it as much because you're focused on winning the money.
b. You wish your parents hadn't made it into a competition, but try your hardest to win.
c. It's no problem – the money's yours!
d. You cheat by distracting everyone else when it's their turn to bowl.

✿ You and your friends are competing on a karaoke game. What happens when it's your go?

a. You run and hide until everyone's forgotten that it was your turn.
b. You start off a bit shaky, but soon get into it.
c. You do a dazzling performance with a few added dance moves.
d. You show off your talent for burping songs.

✿ A friend tells you that a boy in your class likes you. You like him too, so what do you do?

a. You avoid looking him in the eye and go red when he talks to you.
b. You don't do anything, but hope he asks you out.
c. You smile and talk to him whenever you see him.
d. You make fun of him.

- Your friends are making up a dance for the school talent show. How would you help?

  a. Offer to design outfits so that you don't have to go on stage.
  b. Let your best friend come up with most of the moves – she's a brilliant dancer.
  c. Choreograph the routine so that you're sure to win.
  d. You think talent shows are silly and wouldn't enter one.

- You've got an exam tomorrow, but your little sister and her friend are distracting you from studying. How do you react?

  a. Shout at them about how important it is that you get your work done.
  b. Ask them to go and play in another room.
  c. Join in for half an hour and then go back to your studies.
  d. Teach them a new game – you weren't really studying anyway.

- Your friends are coming round for your birthday and you've baked a cake. The bad news is that you left it in the oven too long and it's burnt! What do you do?

  a. Phone all your friends and cancel the party. It's ruined.
  b. Be so upset that your mum agrees to make a new one for you.
  c. Run to the local shop to pick up a ready-made cake.
  d. Feed your friends bread and butter instead of birthday cake.

UNDER-PRESSURE ANSWERS

(Mostly **as**.) **Stress head.** You often feel anxious and find it difficult to cope in some situations. You sometimes take this out on other people, and your friends know to keep out of your way if you're in a bad mood. Don't be too hard on yourself – take some time out every now and again to relax.

(Mostly **bs**.) **Worry bunny.** You don't like being under pressure to perform, but you've developed ways of dealing with it. You like to prepare for situations that you know are going to be stressful, and do a good job. However, if things don't go to plan, you can get upset. Try not to worry so much, and don't be afraid to make a bit of a fool of yourself.

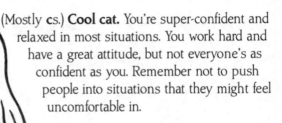

(Mostly **cs**.) **Cool cat.** You're super-confident and relaxed in most situations. You work hard and have a great attitude, but not everyone's as confident as you. Remember not to push people into situations that they might feel uncomfortable in.

(Mostly **ds**.) **Class clown.** People think you're strong and confident, but actually there are lots of situations that you find scary. You cover this up by making jokes or pretending you don't care, and this can hurt people's feelings. Try to let your friends know when you feel this way – you'll be surprised by how understanding they are.

FREE-TIME FAVOURITES

Date .... Time .... Place ....

If you had to choose, how would you most like to spend your free time? Pick just one option from each activity below that you prefer to the other three, then underline your absolute-favourite activity.

Movies. Comedy ◯ Action ◯ Romance ◯ Scary ◯

Music. Pop ◯ Rock ◯ R&B ◯ Classical ◯

Pampering. Manicure ◯ Pedicure ◯ Facial ◯ Hairstyling ◯

Reading. Novels ◯ Magazines ◯ Txts ◯ Comics ◯

Culture. Museum ◯ Theatre ◯ Concert ◯ Gallery ◯

Exercise. Swimming ◯ Running ◯ Yoga ◯ Aerobics ◯

After-school club. Music ◯ Dance ◯ Drama ◯ Sport ◯

TV. Cartoons ◯ Soaps ◯ Sitcoms ◯ Documentaries ◯

Day trip. Zoo ◯ Aquarium ◯ Water park ◯ Theme park ◯

At home. Cooking ◯ Sewing ◯ Gardening ◯ Sleeping ◯

Getting around. Bike ◯ Skateboard ◯ Walk ◯ Scooter ◯

At the beach. Snorkel ◯ Surf ◯ Sunbathe ◯ Sandcastles ◯

TV ADDICT

Date .... Time .... Place ....

Think of your ten favourite television programmes, then organize your list into a top ten, according to how much you really enjoy them. Your favourite should be at number one.

1. ....
2. ....
3. ....
4. ....
5. ....
6. ....
7. ....
8. ....
9. ....
10. ....

BEST BOOKS OF ALL TIME

Date .... Time .... Place ....

Organize the books that you like most into a top ten, according to how much you enjoyed them and how memorable they are, with the title of the book that you think is best at number one.

1. ....

2. ....

3. ....

4. ....

5. ....

6. ....

7. ....

8. ....

....

9. ....

....

10. ....

....

WHAT DO YOUR DOODLES DO?

Date .... Time .... Place ....

The way you write and draw can reveal a lot about your personality. Make your mark on the following three pages then turn to pages 64 to 66 to discover what your doodling style says about you.

SIGNATURE STYLE

First, don't think about it too much, but just sign your name in the box below:

TIME TO WRITE

Now copy out the words, 'This is what my writing looks like,' below:

Now, turn the page and get doodling ...

CIRCLE OF TRUTH

Join the ends of this line, any way you like:

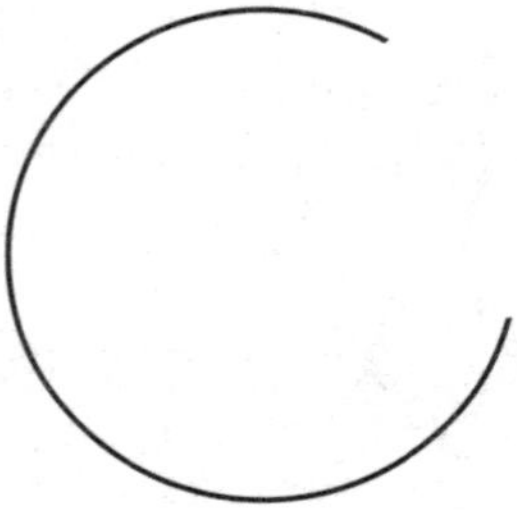

DO A DOODLE

Use this space to doodle the first thing that comes into your head.

COPYCAT

Now copy this spiral in the space on the right.

PIG PEN

Lastly, draw a picture of a pig here.

Now turn the page to find out what your writing and doodles say about you.

YOUR DOODLE ANSWERS

SIGNATURE STYLE

If your signature is large and fills the box, you're an outgoing girl who loves to be the centre of attention.

Ellen Bailey

If your signature's small and there's lots of space around it you're a thoughtful girl who enjoys spending time on her own.

Ellen Bailey

TIME TO WRITE

If your writing leans to the right *'like this'*, you're warm, caring and emotional. Your heart rules your head.

If your writing stands upright 'like this', you're good at keeping your emotions in check and have a balanced attitude.

If your writing leans to the left 'like this', you try to conceal your feelings from others. Your head rules your heart.

CIRCLE OF TRUTH

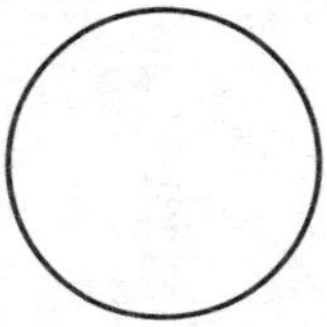

If you completed the circle like this, you're a conventional girl who values traditions. You're practical, sensible and trustworthy.

If you completed the circle with zigzag lines, you have a strong sense of responsibility but also like to take the occasional risk.

If you turned the circle into something else completely, you're an imaginative, creative girl who hates being made to follow rules.

DO A DOODLE

Hearts and flowers. You're all about peace and love. You're caring, kind and thoughtful.

Geometric shapes. You're a clear thinker – organized and good at planning.

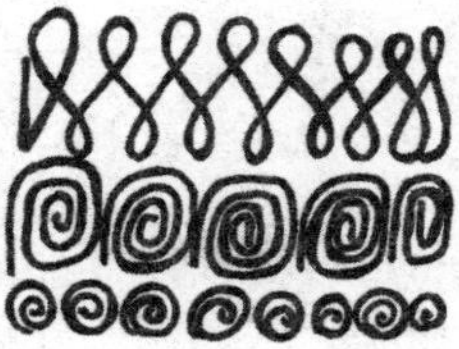

Patterns. You have lots of energy and are always on the go. You're creative and good at paying attention to detail.

People and animals. You're a warm, friendly girl with a big heart. You dislike spending time on your own.

COPYCAT

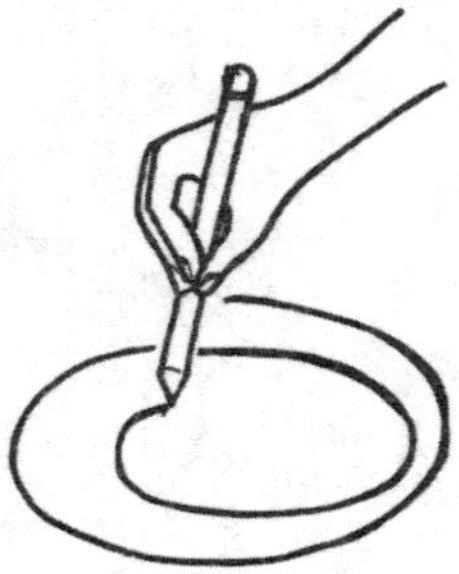

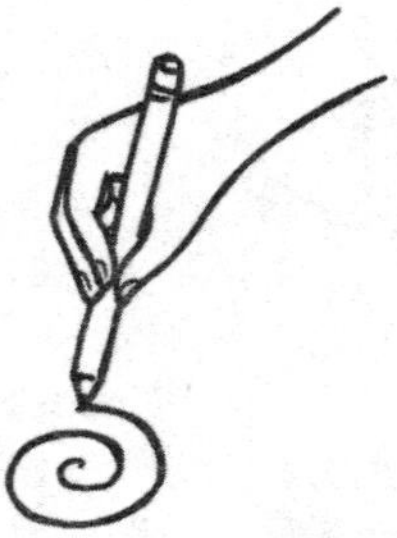

If you started at the outside of the spiral and drew inwards, you like to look at the big picture and think about the details afterwards.

If you started at the inside of the spiral and drew outwards, you like to focus on details before thinking about how they fit into the bigger plan.

PIG PEN

If the pig is facing to the left, you spend a lot of time thinking about the past. You have an excellent memory.

If the pig is facing forwards, you live in the present and appreciate each moment as it happens.

If the pig is facing to the right, you are always busy thinking about the future and what's going to happen next.

SCARIEST THINGS OF ALL TIME

Date .... Time .... Place ....

Everyone's fears are different, so the things that make your best friend squirm, scream or shudder, might be no sweat to you. Take a deep breath, grab a pen and get ticking – it's time to face your fears. Out of each group, which thing scares you the most?

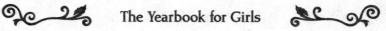

- Slimy things ◯ Crawly things ◯
  Spiky things ◯ Sticky things ◯
- Science tests ◯ Maths tests ◯
  History tests ◯ French tests ◯
- Bungee jumping ◯ Scuba diving ◯
  Sky-diving ◯ Whitewater rafting ◯
- Spiders ◯ Bats ◯ Snakes ◯ Rats ◯
- Lions ◯ Sharks ◯ Bears ◯ Wolves ◯
- Singing on stage ◯ Making a speech in public ◯
  Falling over at a disco ◯ No one knowing who you are ◯
- Graveyards ◯ Caves ◯ Cellars ◯ Attics ◯
- Ghosts ◯ Vampires ◯ Zombies ◯ Werewolves ◯
- Roller coasters ◯ Lifts ◯ Fast cars ◯ Aeroplanes ◯

FIGHT THE FEAR

Date .... Time .... Place ....

When it comes to the things that worry or frighten you most, your imagination can be a powerful tool. If something makes your heart pound and your stomach flutter with butterflies, there's a simple technique to help you conquer those fears, so find a quiet space and follow these steps:

1. First, sit and think about the thing that scares or worries you, and picture it as a bright ball of light inside you.

2. Now, imagine taking the ball of light out of your body, so that you can see it in front of you. Picture the ball turning into a creature or a character that you think suits it, for instance a spider made out of numbers if your fear is a maths test.

3. Next, think of a hero that can challenge the fear. It could be a superhero, or a creature that is stronger than your fear. Imagine your hero next to your fear.

4. Now, visualize your hero fighting your fear. Perhaps she shoots fireballs at it, jumps up and down on it or simply covers it in silly string. Imagine your hero beating your fear and winning the fight.

5. Next time you start to feel afraid, take a deep breath, and remember your hero beating your fear. You could even show your fear character exactly what you think of it by drawing it on a piece of tissue and flushing it down the toilet!

ARE YOU A MONEY MASTER?

Date .... Time .... Place ....

Make a note of the number of times you answer **a**, **b**, or **c** in this quiz, then turn to page 71 to discover if you control your money or if your money controls you!

- It's your best friend's birthday next week and you haven't bought her a present yet. Which would you decide to do?

a. Buy her the expensive shoes she's been wanting for months.
b. Make her something instead of buying it – homemade gifts show that you care, and you can make it more personal, too.
c. Club together with some friends to buy her the shoes she loves from all of you.

- You see a great dress for the school dance in a shop window. Which would you decide to do?

a. Go right in and buy it without even trying it on.
b. Look at the price tag before you do anything else.
c. Try it on, and make sure you can think of at least three different occasions on which you can wear it before you buy it.

- It's time to plan a family holiday. Would you:

a. Start thumbing through glossy holiday brochures immediately?
b. Dig out your tent and get ready for some camping fun?
c. Research online and shop around for the best deals?

❁ The latest issue of your favourite magazine is out. Would you:

a. Buy it straightaway? It's got all the gossip on your favourite celebrities and you don't want to miss out.
b. Leave it on the shelves? You've been saving for ages, and you're sure you can find out the gossip from your friends anyway.
c. Go halves with your best friend? You can read it together and have fun sharing the stories.

❁ You and your friends go out for a posh lunch. Would you rather:

a. Order a full three-course meal – everything looks so delicious?
b. Go for the cheapest option on the menu?
c. Ask for tap water with your meal and suggest you go home for ice cream, instead of having an expensive dessert?

❁ You can't decide which of two bags to buy. Are you more likely to:

a. Buy them both – they'll both get used?
b. Buy the cheapest one?
c. Buy the one that goes with more of your outfits?

❁ Your friends are planning a cinema trip. You really want to go, but can't afford it. Would you:

a. Borrow the money from your parents and go anyway? You'll just have to do more chores than usual to make up for it.
b. Tell your friends you can't make it and have an evening in?
c. Invite everyone round for a DVD party at your house instead?

❁ Congratulations! You've won £50 in a competition. Will you:

a. Hit the shops the first chance you get?
b. Put it in the bank? It's sure to come in handy in the future.
c. Save some of it, but treat yourself to something new as well?

MONEY-MASTER ANSWERS

(Mostly **as**.) **Shopaholic.** You really love to shop! However, learning to save money rather than splashing out is a useful skill. Try to save a little each month, wait until your piggy bank is bulging, then reward yourself by using it to buy something really special.

(Mostly **bs**.) **Supersaver.** Thoughtful and cautious, you are very careful with your money and will rarely buy anything unless you really need it. It's important to spend wisely, but make sure you remember to treat yourself to something fun every once in a while.

(Mostly **cs**.) **Money master.** You keep an eye on your cash and make sure you don't spend too much, yet you're still able to buy the things you want by saving up for them. Keep up the good work.

MUSIC MIXES

Date .... Time .... Place ....

Whether you want to cheer yourself up, or just want to get in the party spirit, music can have an amazing effect on your mood. Use this space to list and order your favourite songs or pieces of music for each category (add who each one is by, if you know).

RELAXING

1. ....
2. ....
3. ....
4. ....
5. ....

DANCING DIVA

1. ....
2. ....
3. ....
4. ....
5. ....

SAD AND SOULFUL

1. ....

2. ....

3. ....

4. ....

5. ....

OH-SO-ANNOYING

1. ....

....

2. ....

....

3. ....

....

4. ....

....

5. ....

....

FANTASY BAND ON TOUR

Date .... Time .... Place ....

Whether or not you play an instrument, anyone can have a successful fantasy band. First, you need to choose your band mates and decide which role everyone should take within your band. Assign each role below to the friend you think it suits most.

- **Lead singer** ....
- **Lead guitarist** ....
- **Bass guitarist** ....
- **Drummer** ....
- **Keyboards** ....
- **Backing singer 1** ....
  ....
- **Backing singer 2** ....
  ....
  ....
- **Tour manager** ....
  ....
  ....

RECORDING STARS

Next, it's time to give your band a name. Circle your favourite word from each column below. Add them together to complete the name of your band. You might consider writing them out in an unusual way – for example, as one word, such as 'Superblueflowers' – to make your fantasy band's name a bit different.

Party	**Funk**	**Kittens**
Cute	**Green**	**Flowers**
Pretty	**Soul**	**Seeds**
Super	**Pink**	**Things**
Girly	**Rock**	**Singers**
Crazy	**Blue**	**Flyers**

NAME THAT TUNE

Now choose the title of your first single, which will go straight to number one in the charts. If you're stuck, use the name of your band as inspiration. For example, if your band is called the 'Superpinkseeds', you might call your song, 'Growing Up Pink'.

First single ....

....

....

Weeks at number one

....

TRAVEL TALES

Date .... Time .... Place ....

- Have you ever travelled overnight to get somewhere?

  Yes ◯ No ◯

  If 'Yes', where to? ....

- Ever been on a ferry ◯ a submarine ◯ a helicopter ◯ a bullet train ◯ a plane ◯ a pedalo ◯ a unicycle ◯ ?

- Where was the last place you went on holiday?

  ....

- Would you go there again? Yes ◯ No ◯

  If 'No', why not? ....

  ....

- Which destination is the furthest you have ever travelled to?

  ....

  ....

ULTIMATE DESTINATION

Date .... Time .... Place ....

Think of four places you'd really love to visit and write one in each space on the first row. Decide which of each pair you would want to visit most, and write them in the spaces on the second row. Now, select the place you would want to visit more than the other: your *ultimate* destination. When you look back at your yearbook, do you think you will have been there?

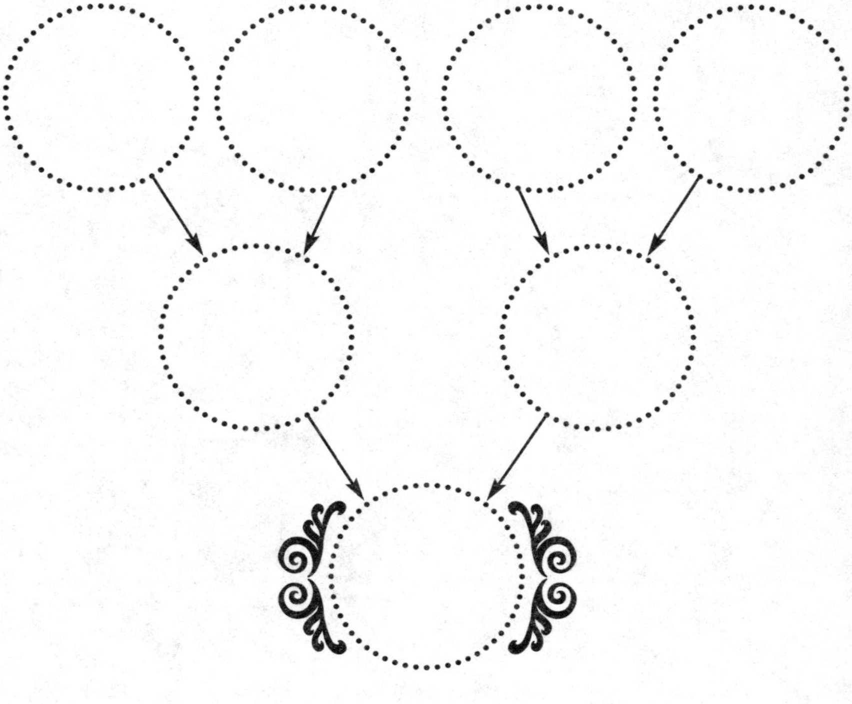

MISS THIS

Date .... Time .... Place ....

Think of ten things you miss when you're away from home. Write your top ten below, with the thing you miss most at number one.

1. ....

2. ....

3. ....

4. ....

5. ....

6. ....

....

7. ....

....

8. ....

....

9. ....

10. ....

DON'T MISS THAT

Date .... Time .... Place ....

Think of ten things that you're glad to get away from when you're away from home. Write your top ten below, with the thing you miss least at number one.

1. ....

....

2. ....

....

3. ....

....

4. ....

5. ....

6. ....

7. ....

8. ....

9. ....

10. ....

FOREVER FOODS

Date .... Time .... Place ....

If you could eat only one item from each list of options below for the rest of your life, which would it be? Tick one on each line.

Breakfast. Toast ◯ Cereal ◯ Sausages ◯ Egg and beans ◯

Snacks. Chocolate ◯ Cakes ◯ Sweets ◯ Biscuits ◯

Popcorn. Sweet ◯ Salty ◯ Toffee ◯ Plain ◯

Crisps. Plain ◯ Bacon ◯ Prawn cocktail ◯ Cheese ◯

Vegetables. Carrots ◯ Broccoli ◯ Peas ◯ Cabbage ◯

Carbs. Pasta ◯ Rice ◯ Bread ◯ Potatoes ◯

Ice cream. Chocolate ◯ Strawberry ◯ Vanilla ◯ Mint ◯

Fruit. Oranges ◯ Bananas ◯ Grapes ◯ Apples ◯

Scary. Snails ◯ Frogs' legs ◯ Jellied eels ◯ Fried insects ◯

Memory Box Memento. Glue a wrapper from your favourite sweet onto a piece of card. Write five words around it that describe the sweet (for example, melty, bubbly, chocolatey, yummy, crunchy, moreish). Put it in your Memory Box.

ARE YOU A DAREDEVIL?

Date .... Time .... Place ....

Tick **A**, **B**, or **C** to answer these daredevil questions, depending on whether you would say, 'I'm in!', 'maybe' or 'no way!' Count up how many of each you have selected, then turn the page to find out how daring you are. So, would you ever ...

	A I'm in!	B Maybe	C No way!
... do a sky-dive?	○	○	○
... swim with sharks?	○	○	○
... hold a tarantula?	○	○	○
... go upside down on a fair ride?	○	○	○
... stay in a haunted house?	○	○	○
... ride a motorbike?	○	○	○
... do a bungee jump?	○	○	○
... fly a plane?	○	○	○
... blast into space?	○	○	○
... walk a tightrope?	○	○	○
... go whitewater rafting?	○	○	○
... dive from the highest board?	○	○	○

DARING ANSWERS

(Mostly **A**s.) **Fearless fanatic.** You are the ultimate daredevil! Always up for a new challenge, you never turn down a dare. You have a fearless attitude and love to take the lead. This sometimes worries people and forces them to put rules in place that stop you taking things too far.

(Mostly **B**s.) **Balanced babe.** You're a brave lady who's not afraid to try new things, but you always weigh up the pros and cons first. You think carefully before taking the plunge, and people give you lots of freedom because they know they can trust you to make the right decision.

(Mostly **C**s.) **Safe sister.** You're a cautious girl who likes to play it safe. You hate being put into risky situations, and are always the first to stop your friends getting into trouble. People respect this, but also encourage you not to be afraid to try new things.

TOP TEN PEOPLE YOU ADMIRE

Date .... Time .... Place ....

Think of ten people that you really admire, then organize them into a top ten, according to how important they are to you. Your favourite should be number one. Write a name by each number, then say why you admire them on the line underneath.

1. ....

....

2. ....

....

3. ....

....

4. ....

....

5. ....

....

6. ....

....

7. ....

....

8. ....

....

9. ....

....

10. ....

....

Memory Box Memento. Write a letter to the number-one person you admire, telling them what you love about them. It doesn't matter whether it's someone you know, someone famous, or even someone who lived long ago. Put a copy of the letter in your Memory Box, and, if possible, send a copy to the person, too. If they write back, put a copy of their response in your Memory Box as well.

YOUR 'INFLUENCES' CLOCK

Date .... Time .... Place ....

Think about the people who've had an impact on you during your life. Perhaps there's a celebrity whose style has influenced your wardrobe, or a friend who's introduced you to a new culture. Write your name or draw a picture of yourself in the centre of the clock, then write the names of twelve people who've influenced you around the outside.

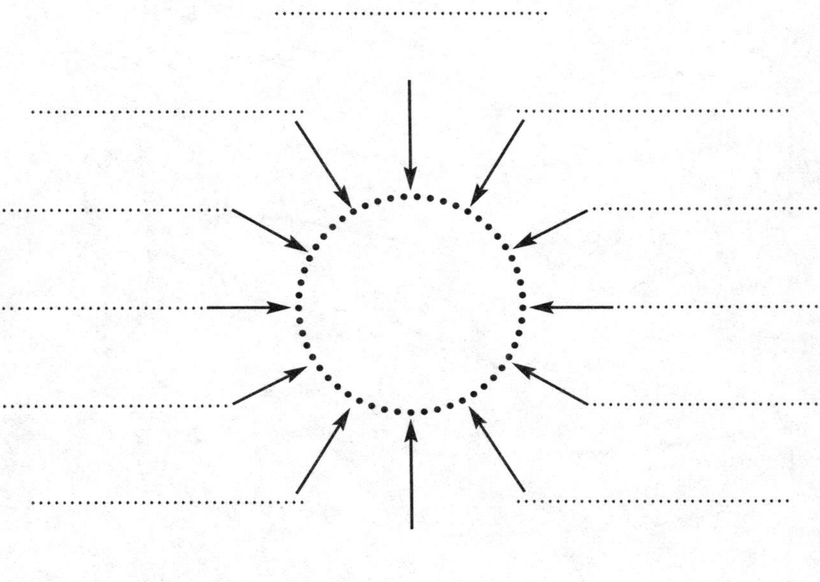

FAMILY FORTUNES

Date .... Time .... Place ....

Ask five family members or close friends to make a wish for you and write it in the fortune cookie papers below. Remember to check back to see if their wishes for you come true.

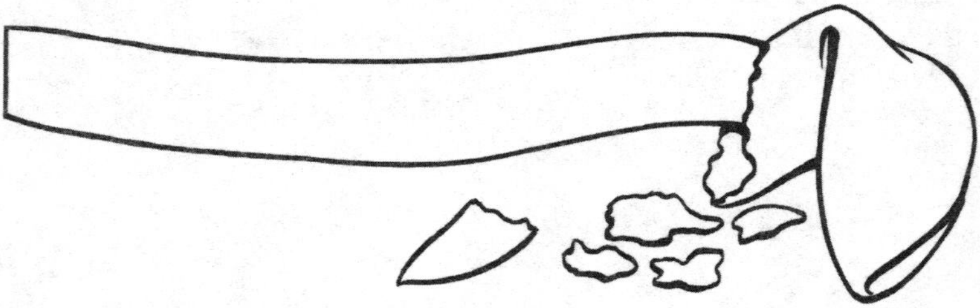

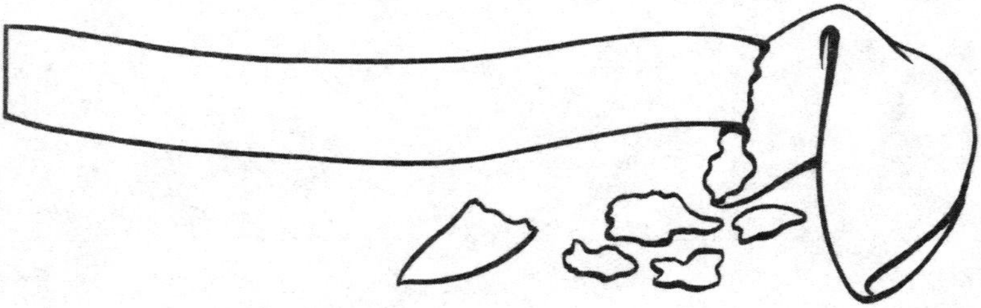

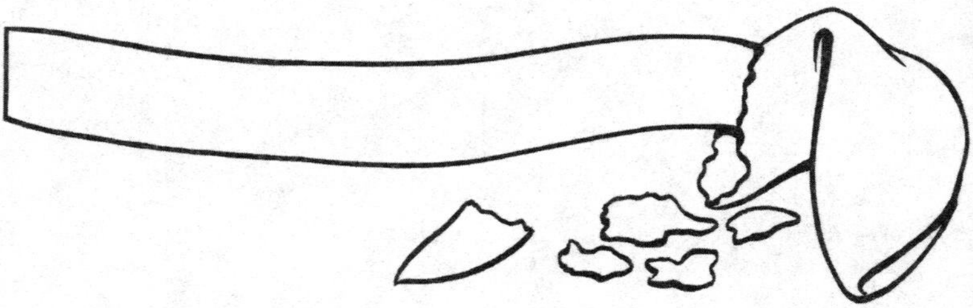

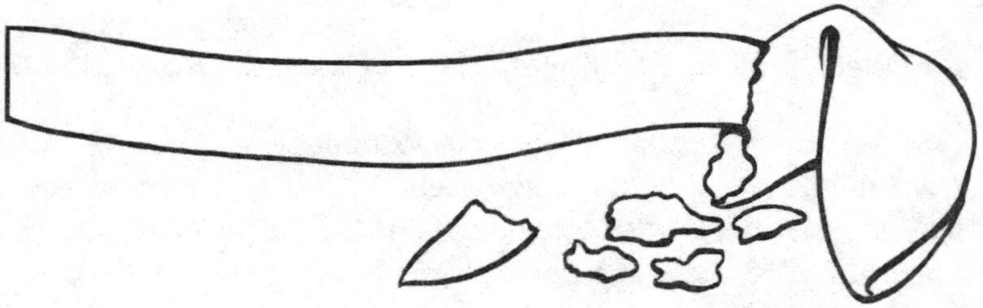

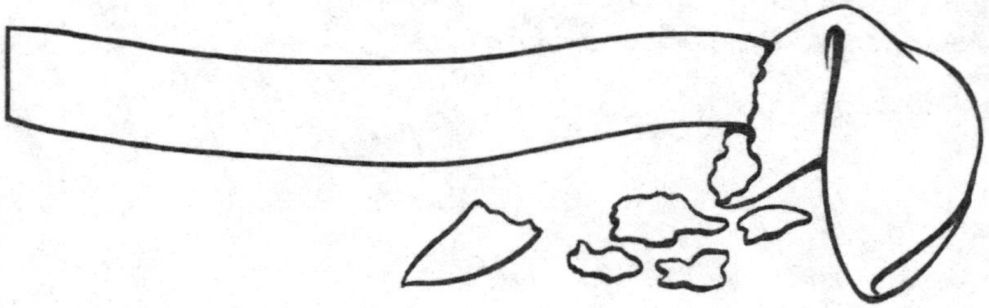

Memory Box Memento. Make a wish for yourself and write it down on a piece of paper. Fold the piece of paper in half and put it inside an envelope. Next, make some 'wish dust' by mixing together as many of the following as you can find: ground cinnamon, ground ginger, cloves, dried flower petals, dried lavender. Sprinkle the dust into the envelope, saying your wish out loud as you do so. Seal the envelope shut and tie a ribbon around it. Put it in your Memory Box and wait for the wish to come true!

IN-DEPTH INTERVIEW

Date .... Time .... Place ....

Have you ever wanted to know more about one of your favourite relatives? This is your chance. You might pick a grandparent, or an aunt or uncle, but choose a relation that you'd really like to get to know better. Put these questions to them in an interview. If there is anything you have been dying to ask, now is the time. At the end of the list of questions, there is space to add your own 'burning question', ready to ask your subject.

- What is your full name?

....

- When and where were you born?

....

- Where did you grow up?

....

- How are we related?

....

- What is your earliest memory?

....

....

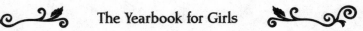

✿ What's your earliest memory of me?

....

....

....

✿ What did you want to be when you grew up?

....

....

....

✿ What did you actually do?

....

....

....

✿ What is your proudest achievement?

....

....

....

....

✿ What is the most important news event that has happened in your lifetime?

....

....

....

....

✿ What is your favourite place in the whole world, and why?

....

....

....

✿ What did you like most about school?

....

✿ Who was your best friend when you were my age?

....

✿ Which person did you most admire when you were my age?

....

✿ Why? ....

- What is the best present you have ever been given?

  ....

  ....

  ....

- If you had one piece of advice to give me, what would it be?

  ....

  ....

  ....

- My burning question is: ....

  ....

- The answer is: ....

  ....

What would your own answers to the same questions be?

Memory Box Memento. Once you've noted down the answers to all these questions, take a photograph of you with your chosen interviewee. Make a note of the date of the interview on the back of the picture, put both your names on it and pop it in your Memory Box.

PARTY PLANNER

Date .... Time .... Place ....

Just imagine you're an events organizer who's been given an unlimited budget to put together the world's greatest ever party.

- Firstly, what would your party be celebrating?

....

....

- All the best parties have a theme, whether it's the colour of outfits people can wear, or a particular subject for fancy dress – what would yours be?

....

....

....

- If you could ask any band, pop star, or DJ to provide the music, who would it be?

....

....

❀ Would there be any other entertainment? Yes ◯ No ◯

If 'Yes', what would it be? ....

....

....

❀ What kind of food and drink would you choose?

....

....

....

....

❀ What would you wear?

....

....

....

❀ If you could ask anyone in the world to go with you to the party, who would it be?

....

....

PERSONAL PROFILER

Date .... Time .... Place ....

Answer these questions, and make a note of how many times you answer **a**, **b**, **c** or **d**, then turn to page 96 to discover the secrets of your personality.

What do you love most about your best friend?

a. You never know what she's going to do next.
b. She's always first to know when there's a party.
c. She totally understands you.
d. You can rely on her to be there for you always.

Your friend calls you in tears. What do you do?

a. Listen carefully and try to help her see that it's not so bad.
b. Arrange an outing to take her mind off the problem.
c. Head straight to her house with a tub of ice cream.
d. Offer some practical solutions to the problem.

Which do you find most annoying?

a. Being made to follow lots of rules.
b. Being grounded.
c. Being lied to.
d. Being rushed into a quick decision.

A friend comes round to ask you to the park. What do you do?

a. Immediately go with her.
b. Call for other people on the way.
c. Invite her in for a drink and a chat first.
d. Ask her to wait while you grab a few things you'll need.

✿ During lunch break, where can you usually be found?

a. Painting in the art room.
b. Hanging out in a big group.
c. Having an intense chat with your best friend.
d. Flicking through magazines.

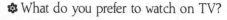

✿ What do you prefer to watch on TV?

a. You don't really watch much TV.
b. Music programmes.
c. Soap operas with characters you can really relate to.
d. Documentaries about amazing animals and beautiful places.

✿ What's your bedroom like?

a. Full of colour.
b. A bit of a mess with loads of photos of friends on the walls.
c. Peaceful – a tranquil retreat.
d. Everything's in exactly the right place. It's perfectly organized.

✿ Your friend is off to a party and asks you to do her hair. What do you do?

a. Create an amazing new style.
b. Let her choose from all the latest styles in magazines.
c. Do it exactly the way she wants.
d. Use straighteners, tongs and lots of products to create a sensational style.

YOUR PERSONAL PROFILE ANSWERS

(Mostly **as**.) **Bohemian babe.** Unconventional and imaginative, you're a true free spirit. Your spontaneous nature means that life's never dull when you're around. You think with your heart and always follow your instincts. You rarely think about the practicalities of situations, which can sometimes get you into trouble!

(Mostly **bs**.) **Social butterfly.** Warm-hearted and easygoing, you have loads of friends and are always the life and soul of the party. You're super-confident and feel comfortable meeting new people and going into new situations. Don't forget to take some time out to unwind every now and again.

(Mostly **cs**.) **Caring and kind.** A great friend, you're always there for people when they need you. You build strong, deep relationships and prefer to spend time with people you love and trust. You're in touch with your feelings and have strong emotions. Beware of being overly sensitive.

(Mostly **ds**.) **Smart cookie.** A bright spark, you're highly intelligent and a quick thinker. You're practical, logical and can take care of yourself in any situation. People admire your down-to-earth approach to life. You have lots of interests and know your own mind, but don't be afraid to just go with the flow every now and again.

BEST GAMES OF ALL TIME

Date .... Time .... Place ....

Compile a list of your top-ten favourite games, in order of how much you like them. They might be computer games, playground games or even games you've invented with your friends. Make sure that your favourite game goes at number one.

1. ....
2. ....
3. ....
4. ....
5. ....
6. ....
7. ....
8. ....
9. ....
10. ....

FOUR SEASONS IN ONE PAGE

Date .... Time .... Place ....

In the spaces below, use words or pictures to describe the things you like best about each of the seasons. Think about the weather, the kinds of clothes you wear, the activities you do and any celebrations that take place at that time of year.

Spring	**Summer**
Autumn	**Winter**

IF I WERE ...

Date .... Time .... Place ....

What kind of character do you have? Are you energetic and playful? Or perhaps you're quiet and thoughtful. Think about the kind of person you are, and the things that you like, then decide what you'd be in each of the categories below. For example, if you are an energetic, playful person, you might choose a Labrador puppy as the animal you'd be.

- If I were an animal, I'd be a ....
- If I were a drink, I'd be a ....
- If I were a colour, I'd be ....
- If I were a country, I'd be ....
- If I were a shop, I'd be ....
- If I were a pop star, I'd be ....
- If I were a musical instrument, I'd be a ....
- If I were an ice-cream flavour, I'd be ....
- If I were a subject at school, I'd be ....
- If I were a fairytale character, I'd be ....
- If I were a sport, I'd be ....

SUPERPOWER SHOWDOWN

Date .... Time .... Place ....

Think of four superpowers that you would most like to have – these could be anything from being invisible to being able to stop time. Write one in each space on the first row. Then, choose which superpower from each pair you would most like to have. Write one in each space on the second row. Lastly, decide which of the final two is the *ultimate* superpower you would like to have.

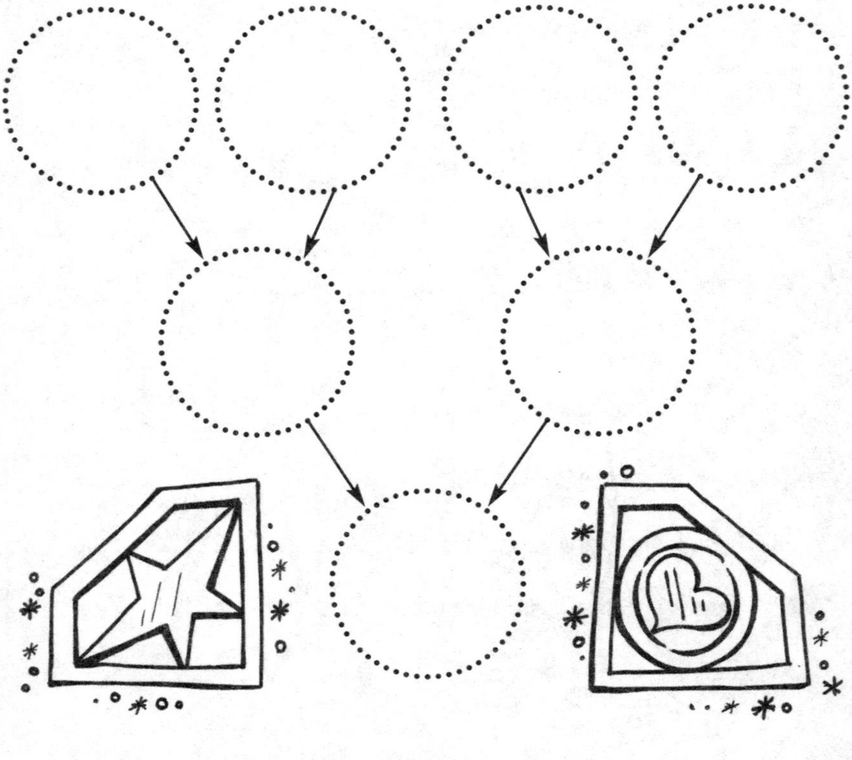

YOUR SUPERHERO COSTUME

Date .... Time .... Place ....

The greatest superheroes always have a super-stylish outfit so that they stand out from the crowd. This way, in a difficult situation people know just who to turn to for help. Design a spectacular costume of your own in the space on the right. What would your superhero name be? Fill it in below.

....

GUILTY PLEASURES

Date .... Time .... Place ....

Think of things you know you shouldn't like, yet you can't help but love. Perhaps there's a cheesy song that isn't cool but always gets you dancing. Or maybe a toy that's for little kids you still like to play with! Write four of these things in the first row, then choose which from each pair you enjoy most in the second row. Out of the final two, you must decide which is your *ultimate* guilty pleasure.

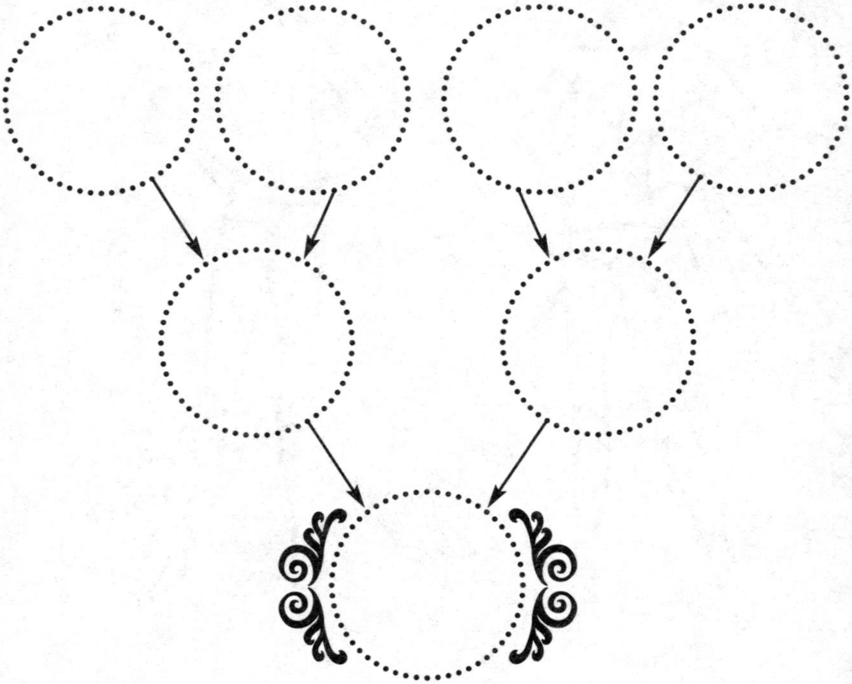

BODY TRICKS

Date .... Time .... Place ....

Tick off each thing that you and your friends can do.

Fill out each person's name in the spaces along the top.

Roll your tongue into a tube	○	○	○	○	○	○
Wiggle your ears	○	○	○	○	○	○
Raise one eyebrow	○	○	○	○	○	○
Touch your nose with your tongue	○	○	○	○	○	○
Lick your elbow	○	○	○	○	○	○
Twitch your nose	○	○	○	○	○	○

Is there anything else you can do that none of your friends can?

Yes ○ No ○

If 'Yes', describe what it is here:

....

....

....

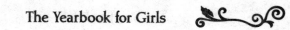

FINGERPRINT FUN

Date .... Time .... Place ....

TAKE YOUR PRINTS

Draw around your hand in the space opposite. Then dip the top of each of your fingers in some paint, or an ink pad, if you have one. Carefully press each fingertip on to the corresponding finger on the page to record your fingerprints. Why not get each of your friends to do the same on a separate piece of paper and compare prints?

DID YOU KNOW?

- Most people say that each human fingerprint is unique, but this isn't necessarily true. The only way you'd know for certain is to check the fingerprints of everyone who has ever lived! In fact, different people's fingerprints can sometimes be similar enough even to fool experts, leading to several cases of mistaken identity.

- Your fingernails (and toenails for that matter) are made from the same stuff as your hair – 'keratin'. This is a protein that is also found in birds' feathers and animals' hooves.

- The nails on your fingers grow faster than those on your toes, with the nail on your middle finger usually growing fastest.

- Fingernails do not continue to grow after you die, as some people claim. It is the skin around the nails shrinking back that makes them appear longer.

- If you stopped moving your hand for a long enough time, the lines on your palms and fingers would eventually smooth out.

Draw around your hand here.

Why not doodle some 'henna' patterns on your hand once you've finished your fingerprints?

HOW'S YOUR 'HOLISTIC' HEALTH?

Date .... Time .... Place ....

'Holistic' is a Greek word that means 'whole'. Holistic health looks at all areas of your life and how they affect your wellbeing. On the diagram below, give a mark out of ten for each question, according to how you rate the quality of each part of your life. Zero is centre of the circle, ten is the outside edge. Join the points you've marked to see what shape they make. The closer they are to a perfect circle (the larger, the better), the better your holistic health.

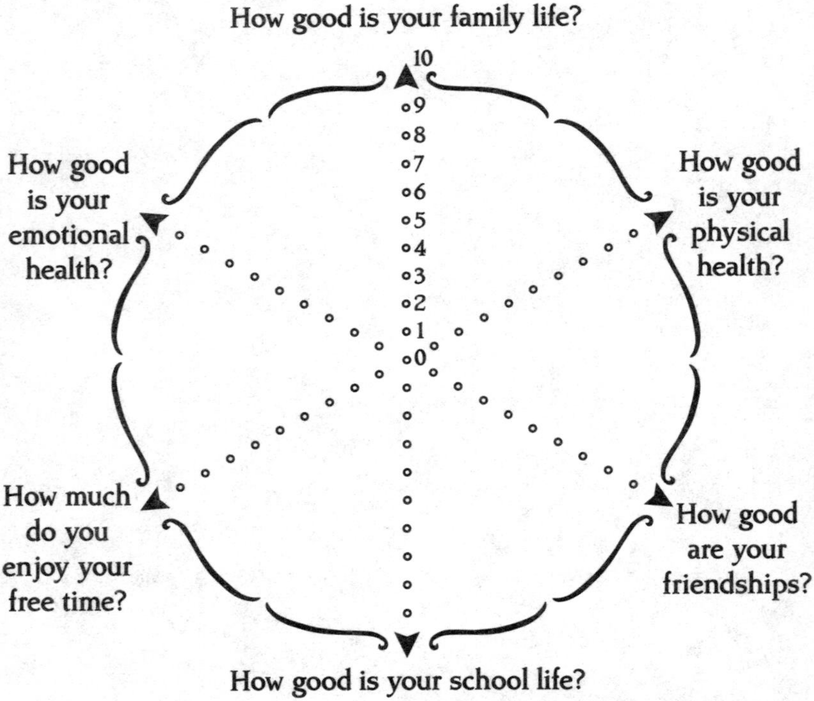

WHAT A WEEK!

Experts recommend that you should eat at least five portions of fruit and vegetables every day, and do at least 30 minutes' exercise. You should also get eight hours sleep every night, but it's important to spend some quality time relaxing, too. Stress is bad for the body and your mind, and laughter is said to be the best medicine. So the more time you spend laughing, the better it is for your health.

Over a week, keep a record of the following:

	Hours of sleep	Pieces of fruit	Portions of veg	Minutes of exercise	Minutes relaxing	Minutes laughing
Monday						
Tuesday						
Wednesday						
Thursday						
Friday						
Saturday						
Sunday						

How did you do over seven days? Great ◯ Okay ◯ Badly ◯

Any areas where you could make improvements? Yes ◯ No ◯

If 'Yes', which ones? ....

ULTIMATE CONFESSIONS

Date .... Time .... Place ....

It's time to confess your ultimate secrets! But don't worry, no one will be able to find out what they are. Here's how to create a tamper-proof dossier to put in your Memory Box.

1. Find a large envelope and write 'Homework' on it in black pen – this will put off any snoops looking for gossip!

2. Find some pretty notepaper and envelopes. Write one secret per page and seal each secret in a separate envelope.

Your secrets might include:

The most embarrassing thing that's ever happened to you, so far.

The name of the boy you like.

Something you did that was wrong, that someone else got the blame for.

Something you'd like to say to someone, but don't dare.

3. Place all the envelopes inside the larger envelope. Seal the envelope shut. You could also place stickers over the seal so that you'll know for certain if someone has taken a peek.

4. Place your 'Homework' at the bottom of your Memory Box and pile everything else you have collected on top.

BEST FRIENDS FOREVER?

Date .... Time .... Place ....

How well do you and your friends know each other? Read through the questions below and fill in your own answers. (Copy out the questions for your friends to fill in, too.) Then quiz your friends to find out just how well they know you. Make a note of the number of questions they each get right. Turn the page for the results.

1. What date is my birthday?

....

2. What is my favourite colour?

....

3. Who is my celebrity crush?

....

4. What is my favourite animal?

....

5. What is my favourite food?

....

6. What do I want to be when I grow up?

....

7. What is my most embarrassing moment, so far?

....

8. What is my all-time favourite film?

....

9. What is my all-time favourite book?

....

10. Where in the world would I most like to visit?

....

11. What would my ideal Saturday plan be?

....

12. Which three words would I use to describe myself?

....

THE SCORES

1–4. Oops! Looks like you need to spend a little more quality time together and get to know each other better.
5–8. You are certainly good friends, but you've still got some sharing to do before you become truly best buddies.
9–12. Wow. You're as close as sisters and have no secrets from each other – you can always rely on one another in a crisis.

AGONY-AUNT CHALLENGE

Date .... Time .... Place ....

Agony aunts (and uncles) often work for newspapers and magazines. They help with problems that readers send in by offering their advice. Why not get together with a group of friends and choose a problem to respond to? Discuss the advice you could give if someone asked your opinion. Practise your own agony-aunt skills by providing an answer to one of the following problems. You can also fill in your name in the spaces provided.

'Dear Auntie ....
A new girl has started at my school and my best friend has been spending loads of time with her. I'm feeling really left out and keep arguing with my best friend. What should I do?'

'Dear Auntie ....
My sister is so annoying! She is a massive show-off and gets all the attention. She is younger than me and whenever she does something wrong I get the blame. Help!'

'Dear Auntie ....
I'm finding it difficult to fit in everything I want to do at the moment. We're getting tons of homework and I go to lots of after-school clubs. I don't want to give them up, but my marks are quite bad. Do you have any ideas?'

'Dear Auntie ....
I feel like I'm always being compared to my older sister. She's really clever and always gets top marks at school. She's also popular and has lots of friends. How can I deal with the pressure to do as well as her?'

WHAT'S YOUR PROBLEM?

With your friends, think of three problems you would like to ask an agony aunt about. Put them in order, with the most important problem at number one. See if you and your friends can come up with any solutions yourselves, or ask a parent for advice.

1. ....

....

2. ....

....

3. ....

....

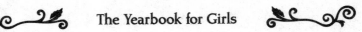

PET PROFILE

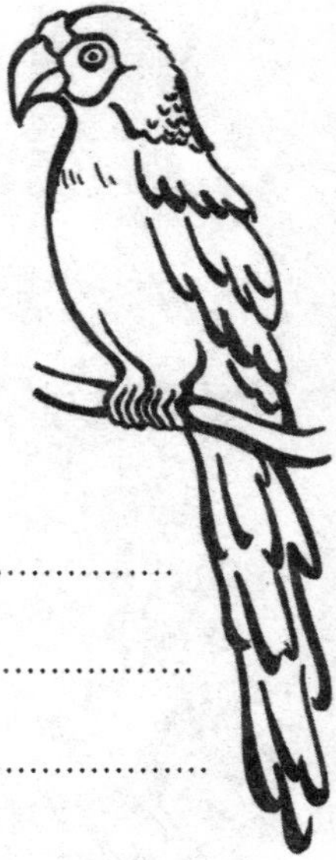

Date ....

Time .... Place ....

Complete the information below, either about your favourite pet or a dream pet that you'd love to own.

Name .... Age ....

Type of animal ....

Boy ◌ Girl ◌ Colour ....

Likes ....

Dislikes ....

What's the funniest thing your pet does?

....

What's the naughtiest thing your pet does?

....

A FEW OF MY FAVOURITE THINGS

Date .... Time .... Place ....

Imagine you are marooned on a desert island. Which items from your personal belongings would you be lost without? You would already have all necessary practical items, so these should be things that you love and would enjoy while waiting to be rescued. Organize your list into a top ten, according to how bored or sad you'd be without them. Your favourite should be at number one.

1. ....

2. ....

3. ....

4. ....

5. ....

6. ....

7. ....

8. ....

9. ....

10. ....

SURVIVAL SKILLS

❧ Date Time Place ❧

If you were marooned on a desert island, but without any essential items, which of the following challenges would you be willing to attempt while waiting to be rescued? Turn to page 116 to find out your skill rating.

	A Absolutely	B Maybe	C No way!
Build a fire	○	○	○
Read a map	○	○	○
Catch a fish	○	○	○
Dig a well	○	○	○
Make a raft	○	○	○
Build a shelter	○	○	○
Make an animal trap	○	○	○
Escape from quicksand	○	○	○
Make a bow and arrow	○	○	○
Use leaves as toilet roll	○	○	○
Eat bugs	○	○	○

SURVIVAL ANSWERS

(Mostly **A**s.) **Super survivor.** Your survival skills are top notch and you love the great outdoors. You feel as at home in a forest as most people would in a five-star hotel! If necessary, you could take care of yourself for weeks on end, but with your excellent navigation skills you'd probably find your way to that hotel in no time at all.

(Mostly **B**s.) **Adventurous amiga.** You haven't had the opportunity to practise many survival skills, but you're an adventurous girl who would love to give it a go! You don't mind getting your hands dirty (or eating the odd bug for survival). Why not persuade your parents to take you on a camping trip?

(Mostly **C**s.) **Indoor individual.** Outdoor living is not for you, and you wouldn't last long if you were stranded on your own. You're accustomed to the finer things in life and wouldn't even like to stay on a campsite equipped with showers and a restaurant!

WOULD YOU RATHER?

Date .... Time .... Place ....

Study each option below and decide which you would rather choose if you really had to – there is no 'neither' option!

- Have no eyebrows ◯
  Have eyebrows that meet in the middle ◯

- Never wash your hair again ◯
  Never wash your pants again ◯

- Be popular but ugly ◯ Be beautiful but unpopular ◯

- Have no TV ◯ Have a TV that only showed adverts ◯

- Never listen to any music again ◯
  Always listen to classical music ◯

- Spend a night in a haunted house ◯
  Spend a night on your own in the woods ◯

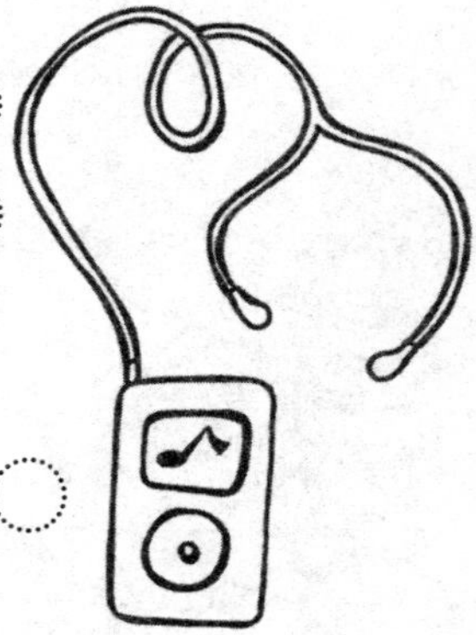

- Have hiccups for a month

  Do nothing but maths for a whole day

- Be able to paint your nails just by looking at them

  Be able to style your hair just by thinking about it

- Burp every time a boy talks to you

  Fart every time a girl talks to you

- Go to school in just your underwear for a day

  Go to school in a clown outfit for one month

- Never read a magazine again

  Never go to the cinema again

- Find a secret treasure stash

  Make a new friend

BEST MOMENTS OF ALL TIME

Date .... Time .... Place ....

Think of the best things that have ever happened to you (so far) – perhaps when a baby brother or sister was born, or the feeling you got the first time you rode a bike without help. Perhaps you won an award that you're really proud of, or you held your first sleepover and it was a huge success. Once you've thought of your five best moments, list them in order so that your all-time favourite is at number one.

1. ....

....

2. ....

....

3. ....

....

4. ....

....

5. ....

....

HEADLINE NEWS

Date .... Time .... Place ....

Have you noticed what's going on in the news lately? What do you think are the five most important news stories at the moment? Make a list and write them in order so that the one that you think is most memorable is at number one.

1. ....

2. ....

3. ....

4. ....

5. ....

HEADLINE-MAKER

Date .... Time .... Place ....

What are the five most important things that happened to you this week? Make a list of these events, so that the most important event is at number one.

1. ....

2. ....

3. ....

4. ....

5. ....

SIGN OF THE TIMES

Ask each of your best friends to sign their name in the space below for you to look back at in the future.

SOCIAL BUTTERFLY OR BUTTERFLIES IN YOUR TUMMY?

Date .... Time .... Place ....

Study each option below and decide which you would choose each time.

- Karaoke queen ◯ Backing singer ◯
- Actress ◯ Stage manager ◯
- All night party ◯ Pyjama party ◯
- Leader of the pack ◯ Team player ◯
- Vintage dress ◯ Trendy t-shirt ◯
- Night owl ◯ Early bird ◯
- Bikini ◯ Swimming costume ◯
- The camera loves me ◯ Camera shy ◯
- Busy, busy, busy ◯ Me time ◯
- Partygoer ◯ Party planner ◯
- New faces ◯ Old friends ◯
- First on the dancefloor ◯ Two left feet ◯
- Giving speeches ◯ Writing speeches ◯
- Fashionably late ◯ Right on time ◯

FRIENDSHIP GALLERY

Date .... Time .... Place ....

Get four friends to each draw a portrait of you in one of these frames. Each friend should write a caption describing you underneath their artwork and sign their work when they are finished.

....

....

....

Signed ....

....

....

....

Signed ....

....

....

....

Signed .... Signed ....

Memory Box Memento. Get someone to take a photograph of you and your friends together, print it and write each of your names and the date on the back. Place it in your Memory Box to look back at in years to come.

THE FILM OF YOUR LIFE ...

Date .... Time .... Place ....

You're such an incredible girl that someone is sure to want to make a film about your life one day. Obviously you'll get the final casting choice, so who would you choose to play you, your family, and your friends? Write the name of each 'character' you would want in the film in the column on the left, then which actor you think should play the part in the column on the right.

Role	Played by
....	....
....	....
....	....
....	....
....	....
....	....
....	....
....	....
....	....
....	....

BEST FILMS OF ALL TIME

Date .... Time .... Place ....

Can you decide which are the ten best films you have ever seen? Once you've decided what they are, organize your list into a top ten, according to how much you enjoy them, with the very best film at number one.

1. ....
2. ....
3. ....
4. ....
5. ....
6. ....
7. ....
8. ....
9. ....
10. ....

ALSO AVAILABLE ...

The Girls' Book Of Glamour:
A Guide To Being
A Goddess

ISBN: 978-1-906082-13-0

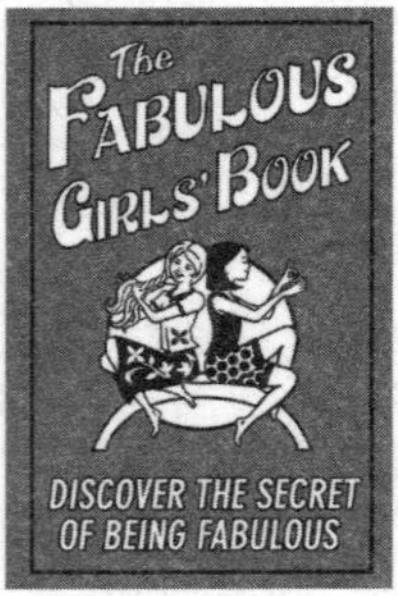

The Fabulous Girls' Book:
Discover The Secret
Of Being Fabulous

ISBN: 978-1-906082-52-9

The Girls' Book Of Secrets:
Shhh ... Don't Tell!

ISBN: 978-1-906082-38-3

The Girls' Book of Friendship:
How To Be The Best Friend Ever

ISBN: 978-1-906082-88-8

The Girls' Book 1:
How To Be The Best
At Everything

ISBN: 978-1-905158-79-9

The Girls' Book 2:
How To Be The Best
At Everything Again

ISBN: 978-1-906082-32-1

The Girls' Book 3:
Even More Ways To Be
The Best At Everything

ISBN: 978-1-906082-76-5